The Adventures of TOM SAWYER

BY MARK TWAIN   RETOLD BY M. C. HALL   ILLUSTRATED BY DANIEL STRICKLAND

LIBRARIAN REVIEWER
Allyson A.W. Lyga
Library Media and Graphic Novel Consultant

READING CONSULTANT
Mark DeYoung

www.raintreepublishers.co.uk
Visit our website to find out
more information about
Raintree books.

To order:
☎ Phone 0845 6044371
🖷 Fax +44 (0) 1865 312263
🖳 Email myorders@raintreepublishers.co.uk

Customers from outside the UK please telephone +44 1865 312262

Raintree is an imprint of Capstone Global Library Limited, a company incorporated
in England and Wales having its registered office at 7 Pilgrim Street, London, EC4V 6LB –
Registered company number: 6695582

Text © Stone Arch Books 2007
First published in the United Kingdom in hardback and paperback by
Capstone Global Library Limited in 2011
The moral rights of the proprietor have been asserted.

Art Director: Heather Kindseth
Graphic Designer: Heather Kindseth
Colour Production: Brann Garvey
Editor: Laura Knowles
Originated by Capstone Global Library Ltd
Printed and bound in China by Leo Paper Products Ltd

ISBN 978 1 406 22493 1 (hardback)
15 14 13 12 11
10 9 8 7 6 5 4 3 2 1

ISBN 978 1 406 22499 3 (paperback)
15 14 13 12 11
10 9 8 7 6 5 4 3 2 1

British Library Cataloguing in Publication Data
A full catalogue record for this book is available from the British Library.

CONTENTS

INTRODUCING . . .

TOM SAWYER

JOE HARPER

HUCKLEBERRY FINN

AUNT POLLY

4

INJUN JOE

MUFF POTTER   DOC

BECKY THATCHER

Chapter 1

TOM IN TROUBLE

Tom?
Tom Sawyer!

If I get ahold of you . . .

Just then, a noise came from the wardrobe.

I should've known you were in that wardrobe! I've told you forty times, leave that jam alone! I'll skin you!

Look behind you, Aunt Polly!

Skipping school and stealing jam! He's played enough tricks on me!

Later, inside Aunt Polly's house . . .

May I play now?

Already? How much have you done?

It's all done.

Tom, I can't bear it when you lie!

Well, I never! You sure can work when you want to!

AAAHH!

Tom and Huck hid in the old tannery.

Should we tell?

No! Injun Joe would kill us!

I didn't do it. Tell them, Joe!

I saw you kill him.

Tom and Huck were sure Injun Joe would be hit by lightning for lying. When that didn't happen, they were afraid to tell the truth. So Muff went off to jail.

Several days later . . .

What's on your mind?

Nothing.

You're keeping me awake, Tom. Last night you yelled, "It's blood!"

It's that awful murder. I dream about it myself.

Every few days, Tom visited Muff. But it didn't make Tom feel much better.

JAIL

25

Soon Tom forgot all about Muff and Injun Joe. Becky was sick!

What if Becky dies? I couldn't live then.

Tom became so quiet that Aunt Polly thought he was sick, too.

This castor oil should mend things. Now, off to school!

Arrghhh!

PAIN KILLER

At school, there was no sign of Becky.

Come on, Tom.

No, I'm sick.

Hang on! I feel better now!

When Becky finally arrived, she didn't look Tom's way.

The life of a pirate was great!

Tom got more kisses that day than he had seen in a year. More punishment, too, depending on Aunt Polly's mood. He was thankful for both.

Chapter 4

MORE TROUBLE FOR TOM

The next day, Tom and Joe shared their adventures.

Then the storm struck, and . . .

At noon, Becky sat with Albert to make Tom jealous. But when Tom kept talking to Amy, Becky had had enough.

Look at this, Becky.

Oh, don't bother me!

Chapter 5
TREASURE!

School was finally done for the year. But Becky was out of town, so time passed slowly.

Muff Potter's trial starts tomorrow!

Have you told anybody that Injun Joe is the murderer?

Of course not. We'd be dead if that got out.

By the next day, Tom was a hero again.

What a brave boy!

HANNIBAL HERALD

THOMAS SAWYER SAVES POTTER

Tom's nights, however, were filled with fear.

The boys decided to try again that night.

You hit something!

CLUNK!

It's a rock.

Let's try somewhere else.

That house! We'll look there tomorrow!

47

The group spent several hours exploring.

Meanwhile, Huck stayed in town, watching for Injun Joe.

I'll follow them!

When the cave was opened, Injun Joe's body was found. He had starved to death.

What are you tellin' me? There's money in the cave?

Honest! I'll show you where.

Tom led Huck to the hole he'd discovered. They were deep inside the cave.

ABOUT MARK TWAIN

Mark Twain was born in Hannibal, Missouri, USA in 1835. An adventurous young man, Twain travelled around the United States. He worked as a Mississippi riverboat pilot, a miner, and a reporter. When Twain wrote *The Adventures of Tom Sawyer* in 1872, most books presented boys as purely good or evil characters. Twain wanted his boy hero, Tom Sawyer, to be a real boy, so he based the book on his own boyhood adventures in Missouri.

ABOUT THE AUTHOR

Before becoming a writer, M. C. Hall worked as a classroom and reading teacher. She has written more than 80 fiction and non-fiction books for children. She enjoys reading, gardening, and walking on the beach in her free time.

ABOUT THE ILLUSTRATOR

Daniel Strickland has been drawing his eccentric characters ever since he could hold a pencil. At university, he earned a BFA in Sequential Art. Daniel creates illustrations, portraits, and develops original characters and stories.

GLOSSARY

cannon big gun that sits on the ground and fires large metal balls

ferry boat that carries people across small bodies of water

funeral ceremony held when someone dies

partner person you work with or do things with

pirate person who steals from ships

punishment something you have to do or give up when you've done something wrong

starve suffer or die from lack of food

tannery place where animal skins are tanned or treated to be used for leather

treasure money, gold, or jewels that are hidden

trial meeting to work out if a person committed a crime

victim person who is hurt or tricked

widow woman whose husband has died and who has not remarried.

BACKGROUND OF TOM SAWYER

The Adventures of Tom Sawyer was based on Mark Twain's hometown of Hannibal, Missouri in the United States. Set sometime between 1830 and 1840, the story shows small town life along the Mississippi River. At the time of the story, steamboats changed the way people and goods travelled. Before the invention of steamboats, it could take months to travel between the major river ports of New Orleans and Minneapolis. Steamboats made this journey in just ten days.

Throughout *The Adventures of Tom Sawyer*, Twain presented the kinds of people he knew from his hometown. Some of these people were important figures in the town, like Judge Thatcher, and some, like Muff Potter, were poor drifters who were drawn to schemes for getting rich. The character that seems different from the rest is Injun Joe. The word "Injun" is a slang word for "Indian" meaning a Native American. Mark Twain didn't know much about Native Americans. He based Injun Joe on negative stereotypes, or unfair beliefs, that many Americans held during that time.

DISCUSSION QUESTIONS

1. Tom and Huck didn't tell anyone what they had seen in the graveyard because they were afraid. Who or what were they afraid of? Would you have told someone? Explain.

2. Why do you think Tom and Becky were sometimes unfriendly to one another?

3. Tom, Huck, and Joe tried to live alone on an island. Would you like to do this? Why or why not?

4. Why did Injun Joe die? Explain how it happened.

5. If Tom Sawyer were living today, do you think he would still be able to have adventures like he does in the story? Do you think he would be happier living now, or living back in the 1800s?

WRITING PROMPTS

1. Describe Tom's town. Is the town big or small? What does it look like? What is the area around the town like?

2. Write what you think will happen next in the book. Will Huckleberry Finn stay with Widow Douglas and obey her rules? Will Tom try not to make trouble for Aunt Polly?

3. Tom liked to have adventures. Write about your own favourite place to explore. Why do you like that place so much?

4. Tom tricks his friends into painting the fence. Write about your least favourite thing you have to do. Why do you dislike it?

OTHER BOOKS YOU MIGHT ENJOY

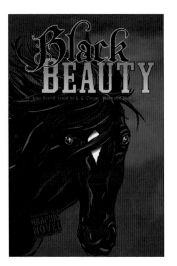

Black Beauty

Black Beauty, a handsome horse living in Victorian England, had a happy childhood growing up in the peaceful countryside. In his later years, he encounters terrible illness and a frightening stable fire. Things go from bad to worse when Black Beauty's new owners begin renting him out for profit. Black Beauty endures a life of mistreatment and disrespect in a world that shows little regard for the happiness of animals.

Gulliver's Travels

Lemuel Gulliver always dreamed of sailing across seas, but he never could have imagined the places his travels would take him. On the island of Lilliput, he is captured by tiny creatures no more than six inches tall. In the country of Blefuscu, he is nearly squashed by an army of giants. His adventures could be the greatest story ever told, if he survives long enough to tell them.

Robin Hood

Robin Hood and his Merrie Men are the heroes of Sherwood Forest. Taking from the rich and giving to the poor, Robin Hood and his loyal followers fight for the downtrodden and oppressed. As they outwit the cruel Sheriff of Nottingham, Robin Hood and his Merrie Men are led on a series of exciting adventures.

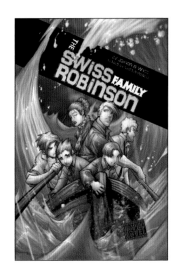

The Swiss Family Robinson

While on a voyage across the sea, a family from Switzerland is shipwrecked on a deserted island. To survive, the Robinsons must find food, water, and build a shelter. Soon, they discover that the island is filled with plants and animals they've never seen before. Unfortunately, not all of the creatures are friendly.

GRAPHIC REVOLVE

If you have enjoyed this story, there are many more exciting tales for you to discover in the Graphic Revolve collection...

20,000 Leagues Under the Sea
The Adventures of Tom Sawyer
Alice in Wonderland
Black Beauty
Dracula
Frankenstein
Gulliver's Travels
The Hound of the Baskervilles
The Hunchback of Notre Dame
Journey to the Centre of the Earth
The Jungle Book
King Arthur and the Knights of the Round Table
The Legend of Sleepy Hollow
Robin Hood
The Strange Case of Dr Jeckyll and Mr Hyde
The Swiss Family Robinson
Treasure Island
The Wizard of Oz